FLORA OF TROPICAL EAST AFRICA

XYRIDACEAE

J.M. Lock

Annual or perennial herbs, often in seasonally or permanently wet sites; stems upright, base sometimes swollen in perennial species. Leaves alternate, simple, linear, distichous, few to numerous, basal sheath open, blade flattened to terete. Inflorescence a condensed pedunculate spike; flowers in the axils of densely crowded often coriaceous bracts, forming a spherical, ovoid or elongate head (the spike). Flowers 3-merous, bisexual; calyx-lobes 3, the adaxial at first forming a hood-like structure over the bud, the laterals smaller; corolla tubular, divided above into 3 broad spreading usually yellow but sometimes white, blue or orange petals. Stamens 3, opposite the petals, often with 3 staminodes alternating with them. Ovary (1–)3-locular, with numerous ovules and axile or parietal placentation; style 1, sometimes divided into 3 at the apex. Fruit a loculicidal or irregularly dehiscent capsule. Seeds numerous, small, with endosperm.

Pantropical, with 5 genera and ± 260 species of which 240 are in *Xyris*. Most diverse in South America, and extending into the warm temperate parts of North America; ± 25 species in East Africa. A medium-sized family of mostly small annual or perennial herbs.

In South America the inflorescences of a few species are collected and sold as dried flowers; otherwise the only economic importance of the family is as weeds of wet places, particularly rice fields.

XYRIS

L., Sp. Pl.: 42 (1753) & Gen. Pl., ed. 5: 25 (1754); N.E. Br. in F.T.A. 8: 6–25 (1901); Malme in E.J. 48: 287–308 (1912)

Annual or perennial herbs, often forming clumps; rhizomes, when present, short, horizontal or ascending. Leaves virtually all basal; ligule present or not. Inflorescence a condensed bracteate spike at the end of elongated peduncles which are often variously grooved or ridged; lower bracts of the spike sterile, occasionally elongated or reflexed. Flowers borne singly in the axils of the fertile bracts, short-lived; calyx of 3 unequal segments, the adaxial hooded and enclosing the flower-bud, the laterals asymmetric and often keeled, free from one another (sometimes fused basally in American species); corolla yellow (blue in at least one West African species). Stamens alternating with 3 usually bifurcate staminodes divided apically into many moniliform hairs. Ovary with parietal placentation (in East Africa). Fruit a loculicidal capsule.

Useful descriptions and illustrations of character states are given by Kral (Ann. Missouri Bot. Gard. 75: 522–722 (1988)).

All the African species belong to section *Xyris*, characterised by parietal placentation in a unilocular ovary. Of the other two sections, *Pomatoxyris* Endl. occurs only in Australia and *Nematopus* Seub. only in Central and South America. However, Kral has cast doubt on the validity of the sections as intermediate types of placentation occur.

Although the species of the genus generally look rather different, accurate identification usually depends on the observation of small features for which a × 10 or × 20 lens or binocular microscope is essential. Anatomical characters may be useful, but have not been investigated for most African species. Characters of value, which should be borne in mind when collecting, include:

Life-span – annual or perennial? If perennial, is there a swollen bulb-like base? Collect if present.
Leaf sheaths – these should be complete and clean; surface texture and colour useful.
Leaf apices – make sure these are present and not grazed or broken off.
Leaf surface ornamentation – spare leaves for sectioning.
Peduncles – spare material for sectioning.
Bracts of the spike – a range of ages is useful; include spare spikes for dissection.
Lateral sepals – the keel may be entire or variously dentate or ciliate; examine dissected sepals from both sides to get a clear view of the keel.
Flowers – do not dry well; spirit material is useful.
Fruits – usually present in mature spikes, but tend to dehisce and lose their seeds; spare mature spikes.
Seed shape and surface ornamentation – seeds must be ripe; use × 20 or × 40.

The flowers of some species have been noted as opening in the morning. Doust & B.J. Conn (Austr. Syst. Bot. 7: 455–484 (1994)) give fairly precise opening times for the flowers of the species they describe; similar data for African species would be welcome.

The family has probably been undercollected in East Africa and this account should be regarded as more preliminary than many in the Flora. Most major recent collecting expeditions have produced either new species or new records for East Africa and there can be no doubt that new taxa remain to be found and described. Areas worthy of special attention include south-western Uganda, the Kitale area in Kenya, and western and southern Tanzania. Various collections mentioned in the notes, and the three taxa here listed as sp. A, B & C may well represent new species but without really good material I hesitate to describe them.

Purseglove 3634 (Uganda, Kigezi District, Kachwekano Farm, June 1951) has the lowest sterile bract greatly elongated so that it is ± 5 × as long as the spike. While the specimen is poor and sparse, and may well be from an abnormal plant, species with similar bracts occur in South America and collectors in SW. Uganda should look for more material.

X. valida Malme occurs in Rwanda and Zaïre (Kivu), and is to be expected in SW. Uganda. It is usually a very robust perennial plant of swamps. It would probably key out as *X. capensis* but the peduncle is 2-winged, and the wings are pilose below the spike.

Fertile bracts red-brown, papillose, with ciliate-lanate margins; a small annual .... 20. *X. sp. C*
Bracts not as above; annual or perennial:
  Outer (sterile) bracts white, pale grey or pale buff, sometimes with a narrow darker median line:
    Leaves and peduncles strongly rugulose; outer bracts erect, thin and papery, more than 10 mm. long .... 1. *X. kornasiana*
    Leaves and peduncles not rugulose; outer bracts erect or spreading, firmer in texture, smaller:
      Fertile bracts irregularly ciliate-dentate on the margins, with a strong dorsal mark .... 2. *X. erosa*
      Fertile bracts with entire margins, with a paler median line but no distinct dorsal mark .... 3. *X. ednae*
  Outer (sterile) bracts yellowish, reddish, brown or black:
    Keel of lateral sepals entire:
      Inflorescence bracts with a distinct subterminal triangular or rhomboid mark; inflorescence broadly ovoid to subspherical at maturity .... 9. *X. anceps*
      Inflorescence bracts without such a mark; variously shaped when mature:
        Inflorescences 5 mm. or more long, ellipsoid or subspherical:
          Mature inflorescences ellipsoid; peduncles two-ridged below the inflorescence; plants usually clearly perennial .... 12. *X. makuensis*
          Mature inflorescences subspherical; peduncles ± terete below the inflorescence; plants usually clearly annual (but see notes to text) .... 14. *X. capensis*

Inflorescences less than 5 mm. long (or, if more, then leaf surfaces rugulose at least in the lower parts of the leaf):
Inflorescences dull brown, obtriangular at maturity; small perennial · 13. *X. huillensis*
Inflorescences brown, straw-yellow or reddish, ellipsoid or subspherical; annuals:
Leaf sheaths rugulose, at least towards the base:
Mature inflorescence ellipsoid; bracts yellowish brown · 21. *X. straminea*
Mature inflorescence subspherical; bracts yellowish or reddish:
Fertile bracts pale red-brown with black apiculate apices; lowest sterile bracts aristate in young spikes · · · · · · · · · · · · · · 19. *X. sp. B*
Fertile bracts reddish, not black-tipped; lowest sterile bracts not aristate · · · · · · · · · · · 22. *X. rubella*
Leaf sheaths smooth throughout:
Inflorescence bracts reddish, spathulate in outline · 23. *X. schliebenii*
Inflorescence bracts brownish; ovate or elliptic 24. *X. parvula*
Keel of lateral sepals toothed or erose, at least in the middle:
Inflorescence bracts reddish brown with a distinct and well-defined subterminal grey triangular or rhomboid mark; dried leaves with numerous dark brown cells, giving a speckled appearance · · · · · · · 10. *X. angularis*
Inflorescence bracts without a distinct subterminal mark; dried leaves uniform:
Fertile bracts reddish-brown, papillose towards the rounded apex; leaves rugulose · · · · · · · · · · · · · 11. *X. rhodolepis*
Fertile bracts not reddish brown; if papillose, then blackish-brown with an acute or acuminate apex; leaves rugulose or not:
Spikes with fewer than 5 flowers, ellipsoid, shiny dark brown · 15. *X. capillaris*
Spikes with more than 5 flowers:
Bracts smooth, shiny, brown, tightly appressed; lowest bracts not more than 0.25 of spike length; spike elongating with age, finally oblong, up to 4 × as long as broad · · · · · · · · 4. *X. congensis*
Bracts without the above combination of characters; lowest bracts more than 0.25 of spike length; spike not elongating markedly with age:
Bracts yellowish or brownish, smooth, rounded or obtuse at apex; inflorescences subspherical at maturity:
Leaf lamina rugulose throughout; spikes dark brown · 16. *X. subtilis*
Leaf lamina smooth (sheaths may be weakly rugulose); spikes yellowish or greenish brown:
Sterile bracts strongly convex, appressed; apices rounded · · · · · · · · · · · · · · · · · 17. *X. sp. A*
Sterile bracts flatter, tending to spread; apices retuse · · · · · · · · · · · · · · · · · · 18. *X. peteri*

Bracts black or dark brown, papillose or not; acute or apiculate at apex; inflorescences broadly ovoid to ellipsoidal at maturity:
Bracts with pale scarious margins:
Bracts markedly papillose, with a long rigid acumen · 5. *X. aristata*
Bracts not markedly papillose, acute or mucronate but without a long rigid acumen · 6. *X. gerrardii*
Bracts without such margins:
Small plants (peduncles less than 50 cm. tall); fertile bracts convex, not keeled above · 7. *X. obscura**
Robust plants (peduncles more than 50 cm. long); fertile bracts keeled above · · · · 8. *X. rehmannii*

* Species 25, *X. aberdarica*, would probably key out as *X. obscura*, from which it can be distinguished by the leaf tips, which are blunt and asymmetrical, not aristate and symmetrical as in *X. obscura*, and the the inflorescence bracts, which are retuse, not apiculate, at the apex.

1. **X. kornasiana** *Brylska & Lisowski* in Polish Bot. Sudies 1: 117, fig. 1–14 (1990). Type: Zaïre, Shaba, Lofoi R., *Malaisse* 13018 (BR!, holo., K!, iso.)

Perennial herb (but see note below), loosely caespitose. Leaves up to 30 cm. long, 2 mm. wide; sheaths about half as long as the lamina, brown, strongly rugulose to scabrid, margins thin, smooth, scarious, entire, gradually narrowing upwards; ligule short; lamina linear, flattened, 2-ridged, glabrous, strongly reticulate-rugulose throughout; apex acuminate-incurved. Peduncles 35–60 cm. long, 1–1.5 mm. in diameter, terete, grooved longitudinally, rugulose when dry; sheaths a little shorter than the leaves, smooth and brown below, greenish and rugulose above with a short terminal blade; spike ellipsoid, acute, whitish, up to 2 cm. long, 1 cm. in diameter; sterile bracts membranous, whitish with a pale brownish central region, the outer 2–3 narrowly ovate, acute, up to 20 mm. long, 5 mm. wide, the inner up to 13 mm. long, 5 mm. wide; fertile bracts 18–28, ovate, acute, membranous, whitish. Lateral sepals curved, boat-shaped, acuminate, 8 mm. long, 3 mm. wide, keel entire; corolla yellow to orange, the tube 1–1.5 mm. long, the lobes obovate, ± 3.5–4 mm. long, 1.5–2.2 mm. wide. Stamens 3–3.5 mm. long; staminodes 2.8–3 mm. long, bifid with tufts of yellow hairs 1.5 mm. long at the apices. Ovary ellipsoid, 1–2 mm. long, 0.5–0.8 mm. in diameter, style 2.5–3.5 mm. long, trifid above the middle. Capsule ellipsoid, ± 5 mm. long. Seeds ellipsoid, ± 0.5 mm. long, 0.25 mm. in diameter, with 14–15 longitudinal ridges. Fig. 1/1.

TANZANIA. Ufipa District: Chapota, 6 Mar. 1957, *Richards* 8497!; Songea District: R. Luhira, just N. of Songea, 29 Apr. 1956, *Milne-Redhead & Taylor* 9857!

FIG. 1. Lateral sepals of East African *Xyris*, all × 10, except 1, × 7. **1**, *X. kornasiana*; **2**, *X. congensis*; **3**, *X. aristata*; **4**, *X. gerrardii*; **5**, *X. obscura*; **6**, *X. rehmannii*; **7**, *X. anceps* var. *anceps*; **8**, *X. anceps* var. *minima*; **9**, *X. angularis*; **10**, *X. rhodolepis*; **11**, *X. huillensis*; **12**, *X. capensis*; **13**, *X. capillaris*; **14**, *X. sp. A*; **15**, *X. peteri*; **16**, *X. sp. B*; **17**, *X. sp. C*; **18**, *X. straminea*; **19**, *X. rubella*; **20**, *X. schliebenii*; **21**, *X. parvula*; **22**, *X. aberdarica*. 1, from *Milne-Redhead & Taylor* 9857; 2, from *Davies* 928; 3, from *Milne-Redhead & Taylor* 9714; 4, from *Macha* 146; 5, from *Paulo* 242; 6, from *Renvoize* 1916; 7, from *Wingfield* 2079A; 8, from *Bogdan* 1383; 9, from *Lye* 6576; 10, from *Mgaza* 142; 11, from *Bogdan* 4664; 12, from *Maitland* 337; 13, from *Bidgood et al.* 4076; 14, from *Tweedie* 1343; 15, from *Richards* 7670; 16, from *Richards* 17992; 17, from *Bidgood et al.* 4127B; 18, from *Gilbert* 5367; 19, from *Greenway & Polhill* 11668; 20, from *Milne-Redhead & Taylor* 11163; 21, from *Wingfield* 4554; 22, from *R.E. & T.C.E. Fries* 2905. Drawn by Linda Gurr.

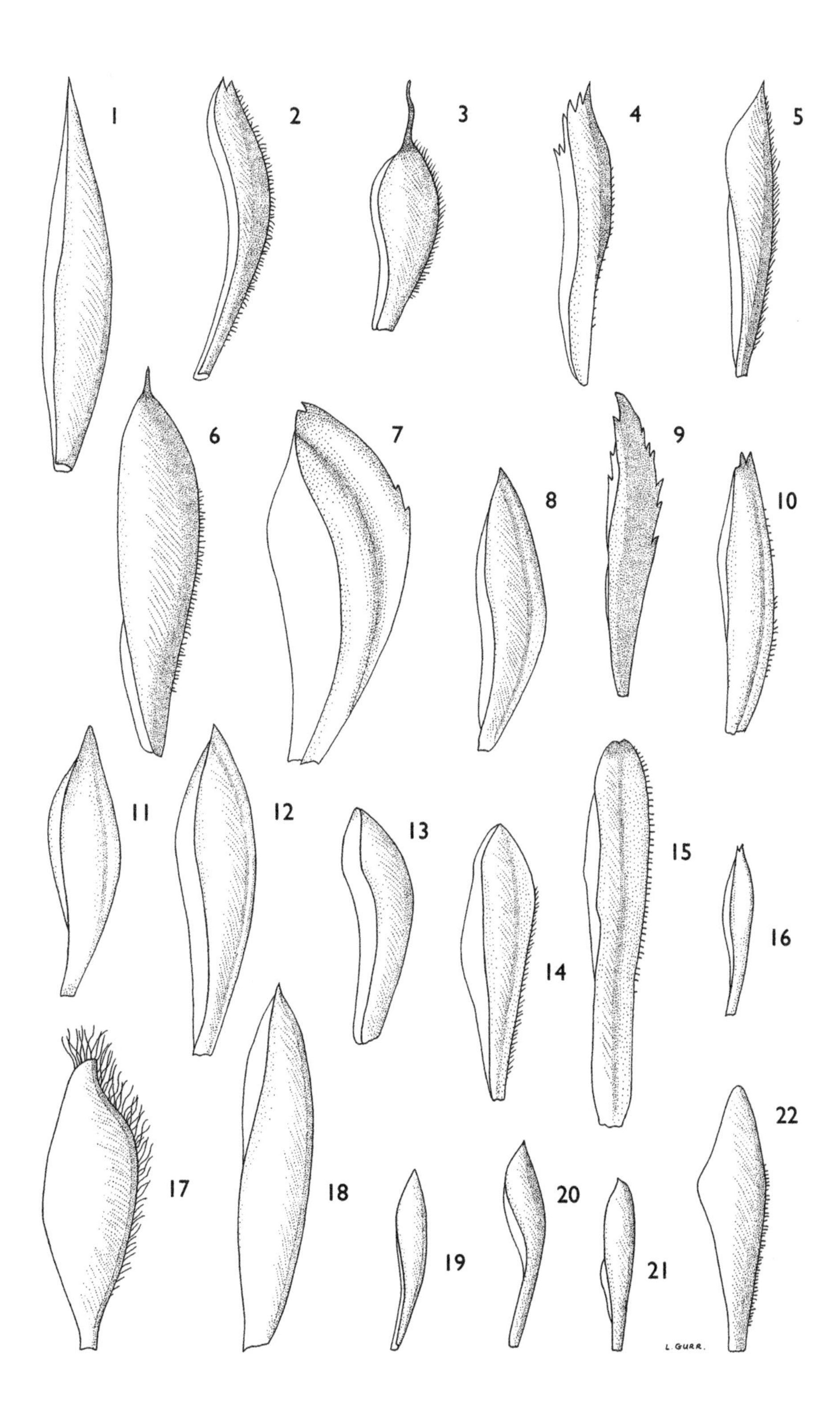
1
2
3
4
5
6
7
8
9
10
11
12
13
14
15
16
17
18
19
20
21
22
L. GURR.

DISTR. **T** 4, 8; Zaïre (Shaba), Zambia and Malawi
HAB. Swamps, probably in permanently wet sites; 1000–1650 m.

NOTE. Brylska & Lisowski describe this plant as annual, and the type could well be flowering in its first year, but both the collections cited above appear to be perennial and Milne-Redhead & Taylor noted it as such. Both East African collections are cited as paratypes in the original description.

Very distinct in its large spikes with delicate pale bracts. Richards describes the flowers as orange, but Milne-Redhead & Taylor record them as bright yellow.

2. **X. erosa** *Lock* in K.B. 53: 885 (1998). Type: Tanzania, Mbeya District, Madibira, *Anderson* 1248 (EA!, holo., K!, iso.)

Annual or short-lived perennial herb forming loose clumps. Leaves linear, up to 24 cm. long, 3 mm. wide; sheaths 2–2.5 cm. long, brown with broad membranous margins, rather abruptly narrowing distally; ligule short; lamina linear, flattened, glabrous, smooth; apex acute, weakly asymmetric, pale brown, solid. Peduncles up to 42 cm. long, ± 1.5 mm. in diameter, terete, minutely punctate, longitudinally grooved; peduncle-sheaths similar to the leaf-sheaths; apex with a tuft of blunt hairs which fall off easily; spike obovoid at maturity, up to 1.2 cm. long, 1 cm. in diameter towards the base; sterile bracts membranous, ovate, acute, whitish with a pale brown minutely papillose keel, 7.5 mm. long, 4 mm. wide; fertile bracts ovate, acute, 5 mm. long, 3 mm. wide, pale shining brown, keel papillose, darker brown with a narrowly elliptic pale central papillose mark ± 3 mm. long, 0.5 mm. wide, margins irregularly ciliate-dentate above. Lateral sepals arcuate, pale brown, strongly keeled, the keel regularly dentate along almost its whole length. Corolla, androecium and gynoecium not known. Seeds broadly ellipsoid, 0.4 mm. long, 0.3 mm. in diameter, with 10–12 longitudinal ridges.

TANZANIA. Mbeya District: Madibira, 23 July 1959, *Anderson* 1248!
DISTR. **T** 7; known only from the type
HAB. Swampy seepage patch on hard alkaline soil in dry *Acacia-Commiphora* thicket; ± 1000 m.

NOTE. This specimen cannot be matched with any described taxon. The prominent central mark on the bracts recalls *X. angularis*, but that species has elongated seeds and a much smaller spike. There is too little material for dissection of flower structure.

3. **X. ednae** *Lock* in K.B. 53: 883 (1998). Type: Uganda, Masaka District, near Lake Nabugabo, Lake Kyanza, *Lind* in *Makerere College* 122 (K!, holo., EA!, MAK, iso.)

Perennial with the rhizome short and vertical in drier sites but elongated, 2 mm. diameter, in floating vegetation mats. Leaves 10–24 cm. long, 0.2–0.4 cm. wide; sheaths half to one third the length of the lamina, pale, longitudinally furrowed, shiny, with membranous margins; ligule absent; lamina flat, linear, glabrous, smooth, apex acute, slightly incurved. Peduncles 10–55 cm. long, 2-ridged, slightly flattened. Sterile bracts ovate, to 7 mm. long, 3 mm. wide, membranous, spreading to recurved, pale buff with a darker and thicker median region, eventually caducous. Fertile bracts broadly ovate, ± 5 mm. long, 3–4 mm. wide, shiny, brown with a paler thickened median stripe. Lateral sepals curved, 5 mm. long, 1.5 mm. wide, delicate, keel thicker, minutely serrulate. Corolla yellow, tube 4 mm. long, lobes oblong, 3 mm. long, 2 mm. wide, rounded at apex. Stamen filament flattened, 0.5 mm. long, anthers 1.5 mm. long. Staminodes much-branched. Ovary ellipsoid, 2.5 mm. long; style 2 mm. long; style arms 2 mm. long. Capsule ovoid, flattened, ± 4 mm. long, 2 mm. in diameter. Seeds ovoid, ± 0.2 mm. long, with 12–14 longitudinal ridges. Fig. 2.

UGANDA. Masaka District: Nabugabo, 5 Mar. 1933, *A.S. Thomas* 961! & NW. side of Lake Nabugabo, 9 Oct. 1953, *Drummond & Hemsley* 4694! & Masaka–Bukakata road, 6.5 km. from Masaka, 11 Oct. 1953, *Drummond & Hemsley* 4735!

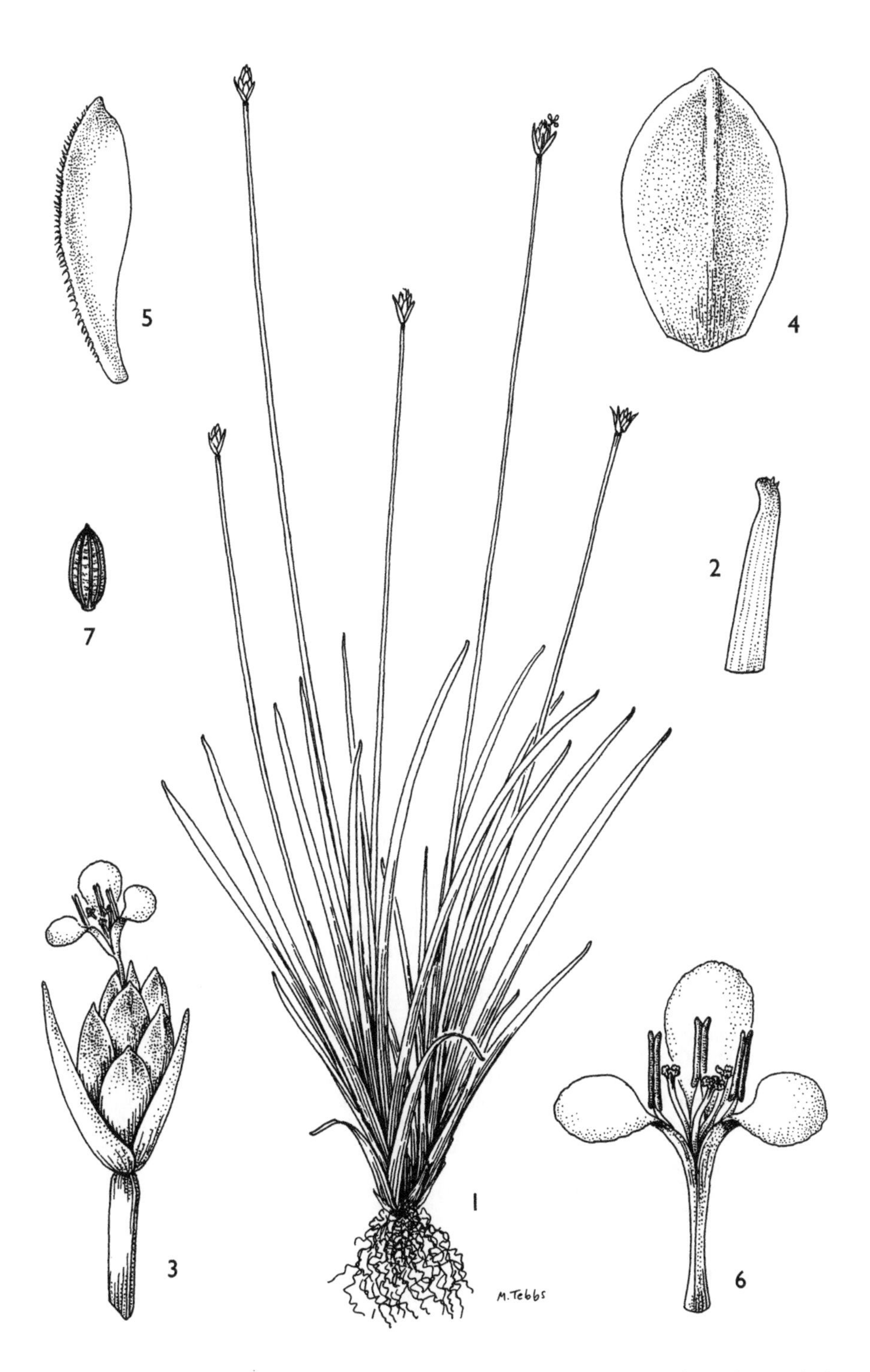

FIG. 2. *XYRIS EDNAE* — **1**, habit × ²⁄₃; **2**, leaf tip × 8; **3**, inflorescence × 4; **4**, fertile bract × 8; **5**, lateral sepal × 10; **6**, corolla (staminodes omitted) × 8; **7**, seed × 20. 1 & 7 from *Drummond & Hemsley* 4694; 2–6 from *Drummond & Hemsley* 4665 (spirit). Drawn by Margaret Tebbs.

DISTR. **U** 4; not known elsewhere
HAB. Grassy swamps, usually with *Miscanthidium*, sometimes in floating vegetation mats; 1100–1250 m.

NOTE. The distichous leaves and 2-ridged peduncle recall the upland perennial forms of *X. capensis* (see under that species), but the pale spreading lower bracts are distinctive. In South America forms with spreading lower bracts are sometimes distinguished only at the varietal level, but given the isolation of this taxon and its distinctive appearance, I prefer to treat it as a good species. The name commemorates Professor Edna Lind (1906–1995), a pioneer of studies of swamp ecology in Uganda.

4. **X. congensis** *Büttner* in Verh. Bot. Ver. Brandenb. 31: 71 (1890); N.E. Br. in F.T.A. 8: 23 (1901); Malme in E.J. 48: 298 (1912); J. Lewis in Fl. Cameroun 22: 46, t. 6/1–4 (1981) pro parte; J. Lewis & Oberm. in F.S.A. 4(2): 4, fig. 1/1 (1985) pro parte. Type: Zaïre, left bank of Congo R., between Lukolela and Equatorville, *Büttner* 583 (B, holo.)

Perennial, often with the base bulked out by persistent leaf-bases, forming clumps. Leaves up to 60 cm. long, 1–6 mm. wide; sheaths red-brown, shiny, glabrous, gradually dilated to base, splitting and persisting as bristles when old; ligule acute, ± 1 mm. long; lamina linear, glabrous, often spirally twisted; apex solid, acute, glabrous. Peduncles 50–85(–110) cm. long, 1–2 mm. in diameter, flattened to subterete, longitudinally grooved; spike ellipsoid, obtuse, ± 9 mm. long, 6 mm. in diameter at first flowering, elongating with age to ± 20 mm. long or longer; sterile bracts suborbicular, ± 3–4 mm. long, 3–4 mm. wide, coriaceous, shiny, uniformly brown, usually without a dorsal mark; fertile bracts similar, numerous. Lateral sepals curved, 3.5–4.5 mm. long, coriaceous, brown, keel irregularly fimbriate-dentate at least in the upper half; corolla yellow, petals broadly obovate, apex laciniate, 4.5 mm. long, 3.5 mm. Stamens 2 mm. long, including anthers 1 mm. long; staminodes almost sessile, composed of bunches of straight hairs. Ovary ellipsoid; style ± 2.5 mm. long, branches 2 mm. long. Seeds ovoid, ± 0.6 mm. long, 0.25 mm. in diameter, with 12–13 longitudinal ridges. Fig. 1/2, 3.

UGANDA. Masaka District: E. side of Lake Nabugabo, 6 Oct. 1953, *Drummond & Hemsley* 4631! & Sesse, Bugala Is., Kalangala landing, 20 June 1950, *G. Wood* Y32!; Mengo District: Entebbe, Sept. 1905, *Brown* 332!
TANZANIA. Bukoba District: W. of Bukoba, 18 Sept. 1961, *Rose* 10030!; Iringa District: Mufindi, W. side of Lake Ngwazi, 19 Feb. 1986, *Bidgood* 26!; Songea District: Ulamboni valley, ± 11 km. W. of Songea, 31 Dec. 1955, *Milne-Redhead & Taylor* 8003!
DISTR. **U** 4; **T** 1, 4, 7, 8; widespread in tropical Africa from Nigeria to Uganda and south to South Africa (Kwazulu-Natal), also Madagascar
HAB. Swampy places, usually grassy; 900–1900 m.

SYN. *X. hildebrandtii* L.A. Nilsson in Öfvers. K. Vetensk.-Akad. Förhandl. Stockholm 1891: 155 (1891); P.O.A. C: 133 (1895); N.E. Br. in F.T.A. 8: 24 (1901); Malme in E.J. 48: 295 (1912); Hepper in K.B. 21: 421 (1968) & in F.W.T.A., ed. 2, 3: 54, fig. 334D (1968). Type: Madagascar, E. Imerina, Andrangoloaka, *Hildebrandt* 3724 (M, holo., K!, iso.)
X. umbilonis L.A. Nilsson in K. Vetensk.-Akad. Handl. Stockholm 24(14): 30 (1892); Malme in E.J. 48: 296 (1912). Type: South Africa, Kwazulu-Natal, Umbilo, *Rehmann* 8139 (Z, holo., K!, iso.)
X. batokana N.E. Br. in F.T.A. 8: 23 (1901); Malme in E.J. 48: 296 (1912). Type: Zambia, Batoka highlands, *Kirk* (K!, holo.)

NOTE. I agree with Lewis who took a broad view of this taxon and included *X. hildebrandtii* within it. Although specimens from Uganda tend to have the broader leaves that distinguish the type of *X. hildebrandtii*, there are many intermediates. The variation of *X. congensis* will be discussed at greater length in a forthcoming paper.

5. **X. aristata** *N.E. Br.* in F.T.A. 8: 11 (1901); Hepper in K.B. 21: fig. 2/9–10 (1968). Type: Zambia, Kambole, *Nutt* (K!, holo.)

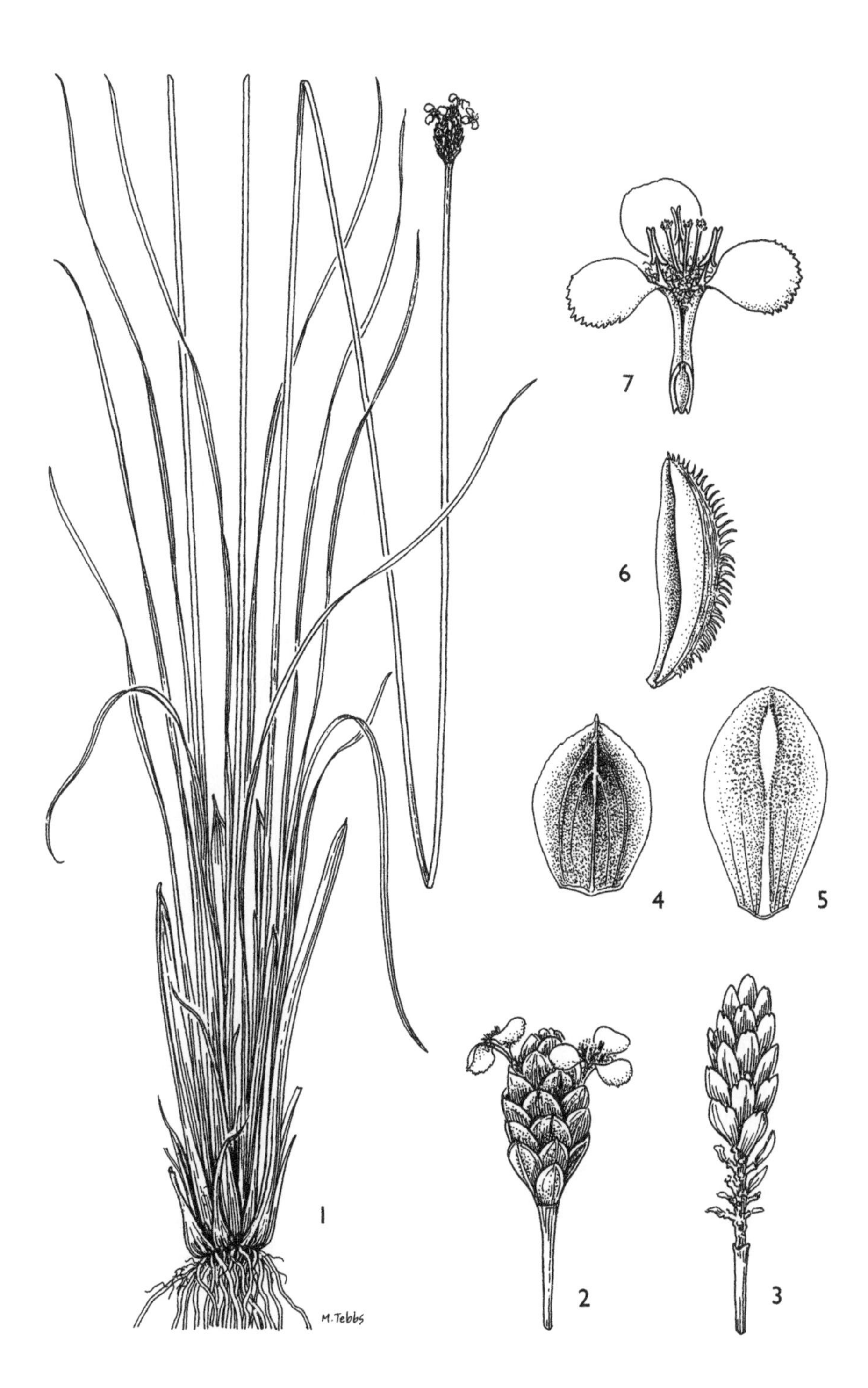

FIG. 3. *XYRIS CONGENSIS* — **1**, habit, × $^2/_3$; **2**, young spike, × 1; **3**, old spike, × 1; **4**, **5**, bracts, × 8; **6**, lateral sepal, × 8; **7**, flower, × 4. 1, from *Verdcourt* 2791. Drawn by Margaret Tebbs.

Perennial herb (but see note below) forming dense clumps including the fibrous remains of old leaf-sheaths. Leaves up to 50 cm. long, 2.5–4 mm. wide; sheaths gradually tapering from the base, black to brown, sometimes splitting into persistent bristles when old, usually rugulose, margins sometimes ciliate; ligule rounded, 2–3 mm. long; lamina linear, minutely papillose, more strongly so on the margins; apex solid, acute-incurved. Peduncles 60–100 cm. long, 2–3 mm. in diameter, terete with 2 longitudinal papillose ridges; spike subglobose, 0.8–1.5 cm. in diameter; sterile bracts suborbicular, coriaceous, blackish brown, papillose particularly above, ± 7 mm. long, 6 mm. wide, including a pale membranous fimbriate margin and a black rigid acumen; fertile bracts similar, or more papillose and with a shorter acumen. Lateral sepals ± 5 mm. long, arcuate, papyraceous, dark brown with paler membranous margins and a blackish papillose acumen, keel irregularly erose-ciliate; corolla-tube 4 mm. long; lobes obovate, 4.5 mm. long, 4 mm. wide, apex irregularly toothed. Filament ligulate, 1 mm. long; anthers 2 mm. long; staminodes 2–3 mm. long. Ovary obovoid, 2 mm. long, 1 mm. in diameter; style 3 mm. long, branches 2.5 mm. long; stigmas fimbriate. Seeds broadly ellipsoid, ± 0.5 mm. long, 0.35 mm. in diameter, with ± 12 longitudinal ridges joined by weak transverse ridges. Fig. 1/3.

TANZANIA. Ufipa District: Chapota–Sumbawanga road, 12 Mar. 1957, *Richards* 8652!; Mbeya District: between Mbozi and Lake Rukwa, 10 May 1975, *Hepper, Field & Mhoro* 5482!; Songea District: ± 3 km. NE. of Kigonsera, 14 Apr. 1956, *Milne-Redhead & Taylor* 9714!

DISTR. **T** 4, 7, 8; Zambia

HAB. Grass swamps, streamsides and ditches; 950–1750 m.

NOTE. Distinctive in its long-aristate bracts. The type is immature and atypical. Related taxa (*X. subaristata* Malme and *X. laciniata* Hutch.) occur in Zaïre and Zambia, and are probably conspecific. Also in the group are *X. dilungensis* Brylska from S. Zaïre, and *X. leonensis* Hepper from West Africa (Sierra Leone to Central African Republic).

Geilinger 2038 from Mufindi (Iringa District) looks annual but is probably just this taxon flowering in its first year.

6. **X. gerrardii** *N.E. Br.* in Fl. Cap. 7: 5 (1897); Malme in E.J. 48: 299 (1912); J. Lewis & Oberm. in F.S.A. 4(2): 7, fig. 1/3, t. 1/2 (1985). Type: South Africa, Kwazulu-Natal, *Gerrard* 1526 (K!, holo., BM!, iso.)

Perennial forming clumps of short stout horizontal or ascending rhizomes covered by leaf-sheaths. Leaves up to 25 cm. long, 0.5–1 mm. wide; sheaths much shorter than blades, gradually dilated towards the base, dark brown with paler margins, smooth, sometimes verrucose below, tapering to a small ligule; lamina linear, flattened, glabrous, longitudinally furrowed, tending to be spirally twisted; apex acute. Peduncles up to 37 cm. long, 0.2–0.5 mm. in diameter, 2-ridged, particularly above, glabrous; spike ellipsoid to obconical, ± 7 mm. long, 4–5 mm. in diameter; sterile bracts broadly ovate, acute, ± 3 mm. long, 2.5 mm. wide, coriaceous, blackish brown with a broad scarious paler margin, becoming lacerate with age; fertile bracts similar but narrower, keeled towards the apex, mucronate. Lateral sepals ± 4.5 mm. long, keeled, margins membranous, laciniate, keel finely and bluntly denticulate, often only below, excurrent above in a mucro; corolla yellow, tube ± 4 mm. long, lobes broadly obovate, ± 3 mm. long, 2 mm. wide, entire. Stamens with filaments ± 0.5 mm. long; anthers 2 mm. long; staminodes bifurcate, each branch with a bunch of long hairs. Fruit and seeds not seen. Fig. 1/4.

TANZANIA. Iringa District: Sao Hill, Jan. 1960, *Watermeyer* 248! & Lake Ngwazi, 7 May 1968, *Renvoize* 1999! & Ruaha R. source, 22 km. from Mafinga near Iringa–Mbeya road, 24 Nov. 1982, *Macha* 146!

DISTR. **T** 7; Zimbabwe and South Africa (Kwazulu-Natal, 'Transvaal')

HAB. Upland seasonally wet grassland; 1700–1900 m.

7. **X. obscura** *N.E. Br.* in F.T.A. 8: 16 (1901-June); Hepper in K.B. 21: 424 (1968). Type: Zimbabwe, near Harare, Six-mile Spruit, *Cecil* 152A (K!, holo.)

Tufted perennial forming dense clumps, often bulked out by persistent leaf-bases; shoot-bases sometimes somewhat swollen and bulbous. Leaves up to 15 cm. long, 1 mm. wide; sheaths up to 8 mm. wide at the base, smooth and with ciliate margins below, becoming rugulose above when dry, dark red-brown in the centre, paler at the margins; ligule not seen; lamina terete to semiterete, glabrous, rugulose; apex aristate. Peduncle 13–28 cm. long, ± 0.7 mm. in diameter, terete, longitudinally ridged; spike 3–5-flowered, ellipsoid, almost black, 5–6 mm. long, 2.5 mm. in diameter; sterile bracts broadly obovate, apiculate, 4 mm. long, 3 mm. wide, minutely rugulose on the abaxial surface, hard, opaque, black with a very narrow paler border; fertile bracts broadly obovate, strongly concave, apiculate, 5 mm. long, 4 mm. wide, minutely rugulose on the abaxial surface, black above, paler below. Lateral sepals curved, ± 5 mm. long, laciniate on the keel above, third sepal ± 5 mm. long; corolla-tube ± 1.5 mm. long, lobes obovate, ± 4 mm. long, 3 mm. wide, apex emarginate, irregularly laciniate. Filament ligulate, ± 0.5 mm. long; anthers 1.5 mm. long; staminodes much-branched, ± 1 mm. long. Style ± 3 mm. long, branches 2 mm. long; stigmas much-branched. Seeds broadly ellipsoid, 0.6 mm. long, 0.35 mm. in diameter, with more than 25 interconnected longitudinal ridges. Fig. 1/5.

TANZANIA. Rungwe District: Rungwe Forest, Jan. 1954, *Paulo* 242!; Njombe District: Kipengere, 7 Jan. 1957, *Richards* 7589! & Poroto Mts., Kitulo Plateau, above Ndumbi Valley, 24 Mar. 1991, *Bidgood, Congdon & Vollesen* 2141!

DISTR. **T** 7; Cameroon, Burundi, Angola, Zambia, Malawi, Mozambique, Zimbabwe and South Africa ('Transvaal')

HAB. Montane grassland, often in rocky places, 1950–2600 m.

SYN. *X. brunnea* L.A. Nilsson in E.J. 30: 271 (1901-July); Malme in E.J. 48: 300 (1912). Type: Tanzania, Njombe District, W. of Ubena, Livingstone Mts., *Goetze* 822 (B, holo. ?†, BM!, EA!, K!, iso.)

X. sp. near *obscura* sensu Hepper in F.W.T.A., ed. 2, 3: 54 (1968)

[*X. nivea* sensu J. Lewis in Fl. Cameroun 22: 40 (1981); J. Lewis & Oberm. in F.S.A. 4(2): 5 (1985), *non* Rendle, Cat. Afr. Pl. Welw. 2: 69 (1899)]

NOTE. Lewis regarded *X. nivea* Rendle as the correct name for this taxon. However, the type of *X. nivea*, *Welwitsch* 2468 (BM!, holo.), is very different; it lacks a bulbous base, and the inflorescence-bracts are thinner, paler, and lack the papillae and apiculus of this taxon.

Bidgood et al. 3609 (Tanzania, Ufipa District, 29 km. on Sumbawanga–Chala road, 1 May 1997) probably belongs here. It is a larger plant with very shiny basal leaf-sheaths, and was collected at a lower altitude (1600 m.) than appears normal for this species.

8. **X. rehmannii** *L.A. Nilsson* in K. Vetensk.-Akad. Handl. Stockholm 24(14): 28 (1892); Malme in E.J. 48: 299 (1912); Hepper in K.B. 21: 424 (1968) & in F.W.T.A., ed. 2, 3: 54 (1968); J. Lewis in Fl. Cameroun 22: 50 (1981); J. Lewis & Oberm. in F.S.A. 4(2): 7, t. 1/3 (1985); U.K.W.F., ed. 2: 325, t. 151 (1994); Lye in Fl. Ethiopia 6: 377, fig. 208.1/14–16 (1997). Type: South Africa, 'Transvaal', Houtbosch, *Rehmann* 5764 (Z, holo., BM!, K!, Z, iso.)

Perennial, sometimes forming tussocks. Leaves up to 50 cm. long, 3 mm. wide; sheaths red-brown, sulcate, minutely rugulose when old and dry; ligule triangular, membranous, 2–3 mm. long; lamina flat, glabrous, smooth; apex solid, acuminate. Peduncles 80–120 cm. long, 0.5 mm. in diameter above, 2 mm. below, somewhat flattened particularly above, lightly longitudinally grooved when dry; sterile bracts coriaceous, opaque, shiny, brownish black, the outermost sometimes with a distinct dorsal keel, broadly obovate to oblong, 5–7 mm. long, 4–5 mm. wide, apex long-mucronate (but the mucro usually broken off); fertile bracts similar to the sterile ones but narrower, numerous, keeled toward the apex and apiculate, the apiculus often twisted. Lateral sepals curved, boat-shaped, acuminate, the keel dark brown, coriaceous and ciliolate-denticulate, excurrent in an apiculus, the margins thinner, paler and translucent; corolla yellow, tube ± 3 mm. long, lobes suborbicular, ± 3.5

mm. long, 4 mm. wide, rounded at the apex. Stamens 3 mm. long; anthers 2 mm. long; staminodes conspicuous, bifurcate, the branches with numerous long hairs. Style-branches ± 3 mm. long; stigmas flattened and lobed. Capsule broadly ellipsoid, ± 4 mm. long. Seeds ellipsoid, ± 0.5 mm. long, 0.25 mm. in diameter, with 16–18 longitudinal ridges. Fig. 1/6.

KENYA. Trans-Nzoia District: Kitale, 18 Sept. 1956, *Bogdan* 4298! & Saiwa Swamp National Park, 17 Mar. 1977, *Hooper & Townsend* 1399!; Nandi District: Kapsabet–Eldoret road, Kingwal R. crossing, 13 Oct. 1981, *M.G. Gilbert & Mesfin* 6748!

TANZANIA. Ufipa District: by turn-off to prison on Mumba road, SE of Sumbawanga, 24 Nov. 1994, *Goyder et al.* 3810!; Iringa District: Mufindi, edge of Kigogo R., 4 May 1968, *Renvoize* 1916!; Njombe District: Lupembe road, Nov. 1928, *Haarer* 1583!

DISTR. **K** 3; **T** 4, 7; Nigeria to Ethiopia, south to Angola, Zimbabwe and South Africa ('Transvaal')

HAB. Grassy swamps; 1650–2000 m.

SYN. *X. dispar* N.E. Br. in F.T.A. 8: 12 (1902). Type: Zimbabwe, near Harare, Six-mile Spruit, *Cecil* 152 (K!, holo.)

NOTE. The staminodes of this taxon dry much darker than those of other species.

J. & J. Lovett 730 (Iringa District, Ulete, below Ghaui's Farm, 20 May 1986) resembles *X. rehmannii* in size and general appearance but the bracts are more like those of *X. aristata*: black, papillose and aristate, but lacking the scarious margins of that species. It may be a hybrid.

9. **X. anceps** *Lam.*, Tab. Encycl. Meth. Bot. 1: 132 (1791); N.E. Br. in F.T.A. 8: 12 (1901); Malme in E.J. 48: 307 (1912); Hepper in K.B. 21: 419 (1968) & in F.W.T.A., ed. 2, 3: 54, fig. 334C (1968); Vollesen in Opera Bot. 59: 97 (1980); J. Lewis in Fl. Cameroun 22: 42, t. 6/8 (1981); J. Lewis & Oberm. in F.S.A. 4(2): 2, t. 1/1 (1985); Koenders, Fl. Pemba I.: 51 (1992); U.K.W.F., ed. 2: 325 (1994). Type: Madagascar, *Commerson* (P-LAM!, holo., BM!, iso.)

Annual or perennial herbs. Leaves linear, flattened, glabrous, tapering to the asymmetrically obtuse apex. Peduncles glabrous, hollow, terete but markedly 2-winged particularly towards the apex; spikes broadly ovoid to subspherical, later ovoid; sterile bracts 4, broadly obovate to suborbicular, pale golden brown with a subterminal narrowly ovate greyish dorsal mark; fertile bracts suborbicular to elliptic, very convex, golden brown with a dull brown to grey subapical triangular dorsal mark. Lateral sepals curved, golden brown, with an entire keel; corolla yellow. Staminodes branched, the branches bearing tufts of hairs. Ovary obovoid to ellipsoid; stigmas much-branched, forming a dense mass. Capsule ellipsoid. Seeds ellipsoid to broadly ellipsoid, with 12–13 longitudinal ridges joined by rather prominent cross-walls.

var. **anceps**

Perennial, perhaps sometimes annual, forming large clumps. Leaves 20–40 cm. long, 4–5 mm. wide, brownish or reddish when dry. Peduncles up to 1 m. long, 1.5–3 mm. in diameter; spike up to 15 mm. long, 11 mm. in diameter. Lateral sepals 5 mm. long; corolla-tube ± 3 mm. long, the lobes oblong, ± 4 mm. long, 2 mm. wide. Stamens 2 mm. long; anthers ± 1 mm. Ovary ± 2 mm. long, 1 mm. in diameter. Capsule 4 mm. long, 2 mm. in diameter. Seeds 0.5 mm. long, 0.4 mm. in diameter. Fig. 1/7.

KENYA. Kwale District: near Mrima Hill, 1 Feb. 1983, *S.A. Robertson* 3509!

TANZANIA. Uzaramo District: Dar es Salaam–Kilwa road, 17 km. S. of Dar es Salaam, 2 Dec. 1973, *Wingfield* 2079A!; Rufiji District: Mafia I., Mwakuni, 7 Aug. 1937, *Greenway* 5015!; Zanzibar I., 23 May 1929, *Taylor* 40/2!; Pemba I., Finya–Kinazini, 20 Feb. 1929, *Greenway* 1510!

DISTR. **K** 7; **T** 6; **Z**; **P**; Mozambique (Inhaca I.) and South Africa (Kwazulu-Natal), also Madagascar

HAB. Perennial swamps and pools near the coast; 0–100 m.

NOTE. This taxon and the next have generally been considered to be one and the same species. The two are, however, usually clearly distinct in the herbarium, and apparently also in the field. It seems wrong not to recognize this fact, although intermediates exist.

The flowers of this taxon are hardly ever present in herbarium material and the measurements of floral parts given here should be regarded as approximate only.

var. **minima** (*Steud.*) *Lock* in K.B. 53: 890 (1998). Type: Guinea, near Conakry, Los Is., Crawford, *Jardin* 120 (S!, iso.)

Annual. Leaves 8–15(–25) cm. long, 3–5 mm. wide, drying greenish. Peduncles (14–)20–45 cm. long, 1–1.5 mm. in diameter; spike 7–8 mm. long and 7–8 mm. in diameter. Lateral sepals 3 mm. long; corolla-tube ± 1.5 mm. long, the lobes oblong, ± 2 mm. long, 1.5 mm. wide. Stamens ± 1.5 mm. long; anthers 1 mm. long. Ovary 1.5 mm. long, 1 mm. in diameter. Capsule ± 3 mm. long, 1.5 mm. in diameter. Seeds ellipsoid, ± 0.3 mm. long, 0.2 mm. in diameter. Fig. 1/8.

KENYA. Machakos District: Makueni, 17 Oct. 1947, *Bogdan* 1383!; Kwale District: Shimba Hills, Buffalo Ridge, 16 Mar. 1991, *Luke & S.A. Robertson* 2713! & Lango ya Mwagandi [Longo Mwagandi], 17 Mar. 1968, *Magogo & Glover* 354!

TANZANIA. Tanga District: Nyamaku, 21 July 1957, *Faulkner* 2030!; Tabora District: Kaliua, near station, 16 June 1980, *Hooper & Townsend* 1994!; Rufiji District: Mafia I., Dawe Simba–Ndaagoni, 4 Oct. 1937, *Greenway* 5387!; Zanzibar: Mwera, 15 Jul. 1960, *Faulkner* 2646!; Pemba I., Makongwe, 10 Aug. 1929, *Vaughan* 566!

DISTR. **K** 4, 7; **T** 3, 4, 6, 8; **Z**; **P**; West Africa from Senegal to Cameroon and Mozambique

HAB. Seasonal pools and marshes and rice fields; 0–1250 m.

SYN. *X. minima* Steud., Syn. Pl. Glum. 2: 288 (1855); N.E. Br. in F.T.A. 8: 25 (1901)

X. perottetii Steud., Syn. Pl. Glum. 2: 319 (1855). Type: Senegal, *Perottet* 809 (K!, ?iso.)

X. humilis Kunth β *minima* (Steud.) L.A. Nilsson in Öfvers. K. Vetensk.-Akad. Förhandl. Stockholm 1891: 152 (1891)

X. humilis Kunth var. *minima* (Steud.) T. Durand & Schinz, Consp. Fl. Afr. 5: 420 (1895)

[*X. anceps* sensu Hepper in K.B. 21: 419 (1968) & in F.W.T.A., ed. 2, 3: 54, fig. 334C (1968); Vollesen in Opera Bot. 59: 97 (1980); J. Lewis in Fl. Cameroun 22: 42, t. 6/8 (1981); U.K.W.F., ed. 2: 325 (1994), *non* Lam. sensu stricto]

NOTE. Always smaller than the nominate variety, and apparently always annual. Very small forms may be distinguished from other small taxa by the green patch at the apex of the outer bracts.

Bidgood et al. 4126 (Tanzania, Mpanda District, 56 km. on Uvinza–Mpanda road, 21 May 1997) may represent a related taxon. It is a rather similar small annual, but the keels of the lateral sepals are spinulose, the petals are apparently larger (4 x 5.5 mm.), and the spikes are red-tinged throughout.

10. **X. angularis** *N.E. Br.* in F.T.A. 8: 22 (1901). Type: Nigeria, Nupe, *Barter* (K!, holo.)

Perennial herb forming loose clumps. Leaves 8–15(–40) cm. long, 3–4 mm. wide; sheaths lightly furrowed, brown, glabrous, with narrow scarious margins; ligule acute, ± 1 mm. long; lamina linear, glabrous, smooth or minutely rugulose on one surface, dark-speckled when dry; apex acute, straight or slightly incurved, serrulate, sometimes with a group of small finger-like hairs at the extreme tip. Peduncles 20–50(–85) cm. long, 1–1.5 mm. in diameter, terete with 4–6 longitudinal ridges, glabrous; spike subspherical to broadly ellipsoid, up to 8 mm. long, 8 mm. in diameter, at maturity, reddish brown; the four outermost sterile bracts very broadly ovate, ± 2 mm. long and wide, apex rounded; other sterile bracts broadly ovate, 5 mm. long, 3.5 mm. wide, coriaceous, reddish brown with a very distinct grey central area, margins laciniate-ciliate, apex rounded, sometimes with a distinct tuft of arachnose hairs, later glabrous; fertile bracts similar but larger, 5 mm. long, 3.5 mm. wide. Lateral sepals arcuate, 4.5 mm. long, 1 mm. wide, keel ciliate-dentate, sometimes with an apical tuft of hairs; corolla yellow, tube ± 3 mm. long, lobes oblong, ± 3.5 mm. long, 1.5 mm. wide, dentate at the apex. Stamens ± 1 mm. long; anther 0.5 mm. long, lobes spreading below; staminodes small bunches of hairs. Ovary oblong, ± 2 mm. long, 0.5 mm.; style 4 mm. long, 3-branched in upper third; stigmas many-lobed. Seeds narrowly ellipsoid, ± 1 mm. long, 0.25 mm. in diameter, with numerous irregular longitudinal ridges or reticulations. Fig. 1/9.

UGANDA. Masaka District: Makonzi–Kasala in Jubiya Forest, 12 Aug. 1971, *Lye & Katende* 6576! & NW. side of Lake Nabugabo, 9 Oct. 1953, *Drummond & Hemsley* 4687! & Bugabo, SW. of Lake Nabugabo, 1 Feb. 1969, *Lye, Morrison & Lester* 1829!
TANZANIA. Songea District: 6.5 km. E. of Gumbiro, 25 Jan. 1956, *Milne-Redhead & Taylor* 8428!
DISTR. **U** 4, **T** 8; Nigeria, Cameroon, Zaïre, Burundi, Angola and Zambia
HAB. Seasonally or permanently wet sandy grassland or woodland, swamp edges; 950–1200 m.

SYN. *X. vanderystii* Malme in Arkiv Bot. 22A, 4: 3 (1928). Types: Zaïre, Kimbambi, *Vanderyst* 1476 & 14745 & Kalchaka, *Vanderyst* 2840 & Atene, *Vanderyst* 3144 & 3431bis & NDembo, *Vanderyst* (all BR!, syn.)
X. decipiens N.E. Br. var. *vanderystii* (Malme) Malme in Arkiv Bot. 24A, 5: 2 (1932)
[*X. decipiens* sensu Hepper in F.W.T.A., ed. 2, 3: 55 (1967); J. Lewis in Fl. Cameroun 22: 45 (1981), *non* N.E. Br. in Fl. Cap. 7:3 (1897)]

NOTE. Hepper and Lewis regarded this as synonymous with *X. decipiens*. Material from West Africa named as *X. decipiens* has very much larger spikes, and the central pale area of the bracts has reticulate veining on each side of the prominent midrib. I believe that it is more satisfactory to keep the two taxa separate until a full revision is carried out. The elongated seeds of *X. angularis* are also distinctive.

The Tanzanian specimen has hairier bracts than the Uganda material. Bract hairiness varies considerably with age; mature fruiting spikes may be almost glabrous and larger than when young, as in the type.

11. **X. rhodolepis** (*Malme*) *Lock* in K.B. 53: 886 (1998). Types: Angola, Domba–Cuanaval R., *Gossweiler* 2817 (BM!, syn.) & I'Chancambe R., Cuanaval R., *Gossweiler* 2644 (BM!, syn.) & between Mt. Amaral and Maria Pia, *Gossweiler* 1829A (BM!, syn.)

Small tufted perennial. Leaves 3–5(–8) cm. long, 1 mm. wide; sheaths brown, rugulose, appressed-rufous-pilose at the extreme base, ciliate on the margins and irregularly ciliate on the 2 dorsal ridges; lamina linear, flattened, rugulose throughout; apex acute, solid, smooth. Peduncles 14–30 cm. long, terete, smooth, glabrous; spike obovoid, 5–6 mm. long, dark red-brown; outer sterile bracts elliptic, ± 4 mm. long, 2 mm. wide, red-brown, apex obtuse, with a single strong nerve, inner similar but thinner and 3-nerved; fertile bracts similar but broader and thinner, often papillose towards the apex. Lateral sepals ± 4 mm. long, 1 mm. wide, strongly keeled, the keel irregularly ciliate-toothed, the teeth below the middle often directed downwards, red-brown, the keel darker; apex apiculate; corolla-lobes broadly obovate, ± 3.5 mm. long, 3 mm. wide. Filaments ± 0.5 mm. long; anthers ± 1 mm. long; staminodes a bunch of hairs. Style trifid. Seeds ellipsoid to ovoid, 0.5 mm. long, 0.25 mm. in diameter, with ± 12 longitudinal ridges. Fig. 1/10.

TANZANIA. Songea District: Luhira valley, Sept. 1956, *Mgaza* 142!
DISTR. **T** 8; Zaïre, Angola, Zambia, Malawi, Mozambique and Zimbabwe
HAB. Moist grasslands; ± 1200 m.

SYN. *X. humpatensis* N.E. Br. var. *rhodolepis* Malme in Arkiv. Bot. 24A, 5: 7 (1932)

NOTE. An inconspicuous and somewhat nondescript species, superficially very similar to *X. huillensis*, but differing in the rugulose leaves and leaf-sheaths, in the long reddish brown sterile bracts of the spike and in the irregularly ciliate-dentate keel of the lateral sepals. The wide scattering of single collections suggests that this species is either everywhere scarce, or else overlooked.

Details of the flowers and seeds have been taken from *Fanshawe* F1498 (EA, K) from Chingola, Zambia.

12. **X. makuensis** *N.E. Br.* in F.T.A. 8: 17 (1902); Malme in E.J. 48: 304 (1912). Type: Mozambique, Namuli Mts., *Last* (K!, holo., BM!, iso.)

Perennial forming clumps; rhizomes sometimes present, upright or ascending. Leaves 3–18 cm. long, 1 mm. wide; sheaths pale brown, smooth, glabrous, gradually tapered to the apex; ligule absent; lamina flattened, glabrous, smooth or with minutely denticulate margins; apex solid, acute, sometimes incurved. Peduncle 10–26 cm. long, smooth, terete, weakly 2-ridged above; spike ellipsoid, 5–6 mm. long; bracts dark brown, with an almost black midrib forming a keel towards the apex and excurrent as a mucro; lowest sterile bracts elliptic, ± 2.5 mm. long, 1.5 mm. wide; upper sterile bracts elliptic, 3.5 mm. long, 2 mm. wide; fertile bracts 4.5 mm. long, 2.5 mm. wide. Lateral sepals slightly curved, ± 5.2 mm. long, 1 mm. wide; pale brown, keel entire, very dark, particularly towards the apex; corolla-lobes suborbicular, ± 4.5 mm. in diameter, apex (?always) dentate. Filaments ± 1 mm. long; anthers 1.5 mm. long; staminodes much-branched, forming dense tufts of hairs. Ovary obovoid, ± 3 mm. long; style 5.5 mm. long in total, branches 2.5 mm. long; stigmas peltate, many-lobed. Seeds ellipsoid, 0.6–0.7 mm. long, with ± 12 longitudinal ridges.

TANZANIA. "Zanzibar to Uyui", *W.E. Taylor*
DISTR. **T** ?5; Malawi and Mozambique
HAB. Upland grassland and marsh

NOTE. Most collections of this species are from Mt. Mlanje in Malawi but it may be more widespread. N.E. Brown cited several specimens in his description but the *Last* specimen at Kew is annotated as the type by him. The locality of Taylor's material is uncertain and may be incorrect; the species has not been collected again in the Flora area.

13. **X. huillensis** *Rendle*, Cat. Afr. Pl. Welw. 2: 71 (1899). Types: Angola, Huilla, Empalanca, *Welwitsch* 2469 (BM!, K!, syn.) & between Nene and Humpata, near Quipumpualine R., *Welwitsch* 2472 (BM!, syn.)

Small tufted perennial. Leaves 5–8(–11) cm. long, 1 mm. wide; sheaths brown, smooth, glabrous except for ciliate margins below; ligule not seen; lamina linear, smooth, glabrous; apex acute, solid, smooth. Peduncles 20–30 cm. long, terete, glabrous, smooth, weakly grooved longitudinally; sheaths smooth, shorter than the leaves; spike ellipsoid, later obtriangular, dark brown, 4–5 mm. long; outer sterile bracts obovate, 3.5 mm. long, 1.8 mm. wide, brown, keeled towards the emarginate apex, nerve strong but poorly defined, excurrent as a mucro, inner sterile bracts similar but nerve less prominent and apiculus lacking, apex often splitting but probably not truly laciniate; fertile bracts similar but thinner and more concave. Lateral sepals boat-shaped, 3.5 mm. long, 0.8 mm. wide, pale brown, darker on the entire glabrous keel; corolla yellow, tube 3 mm. long; lobes oblong, 2 mm. long, 1 mm. Stamens 1 mm. long including 0.5 mm. anthers; staminodes bunches of hairs. Ovary obovoid, 2 mm. long, 1 mm. in diameter; style 3 mm. long, the upper third trifid; stigmas 2–3-lobed. Capsule obovoid, 6 mm. long. Seeds ellipsoid, 0.5 mm. long, 0.3 mm. in diameter, longitudinally ridged. Fig. 1/11.

KENYA. Trans-Nzoia District: 3 km. W. of Kitale, 5 Oct. 1958, *Bogdan* 4664! & Kitale, 18 Sept. 1956, *Bogdan* 4297!; Uasin Gishu District: Kipkarren, Mar. 1932, *Brodhurst Hill* 7121
TANZANIA. Moshi District: Kilimanjaro, Kiwira Middle fishing camp, 4 Nov. 1993, *Grimshaw* 931044!; Iringa District: Mufindi, 4–5 km. S. of Lake Ngwazi, 28 Aug. 1986, *Linder* 3830!; Tunduru District: W. of Puchapucha and 1.5 km. E. of R. Muhuwesi [Mawese], 19 Dec. 1955, *Milne-Redhead & Taylor* 7716!
DISTR. **K** 3; **T** 2, 4, ?5 (see note), 7, 8; Angola and Malawi
HAB. Marshy places, often on sandy soil; 950–2250 m.

SYN. *X. capensis* Thunb. var. *medullosa* N.E. Br. in F.T.A. 8: 14 (1901). Type: Tanzania, without further locality, *Hannington* (K!, holo.)

NOTE. Hannington's rather fragmentary specimen is unlocalised. According to the biography of Hannnington by Dawson, he collected mainly in the Mpwapwa area, but also travelled on to Uyui (near Tabora) and then to Lake Victoria. Possibly **T** 5 should be added to the distribution.

Lewis, when labelling herbarium sheets, often applied the varietal name to small plants which are here treated as *X. rubella* and *X. schliebenii*. In Fl. Cameroun he placed *X. capensis* var. *medullosa* as a synonym of *X. capensis*; in F.S.A. he does not mention it but treats *X. rubella* as a synonym of *X. capensis*. See under *X. rubella* for further discussion.

A small and rather nondescript taxon. *Haarer* 1660 was seen by Malme, who annotated it as '*Species nova e stirpe X. capensis*'. He did not connect it with N.E. Brown's variety, nor with *X. huillensis*.

14. **X. capensis** *Thunb.*, Prodr. Pl. Cap.: 12 (1794); Malme in E.J. 48: 305 (1912); Hepper in F.W.T.A., ed. 2, 3: 54 (1968); J. Lewis in Fl. Cameroun 22: 37 (1981); J. Lewis & Oberm. in F.S.A. 4(2): 2, fig. 1/2 (1985); Troupin, Fl. Rwanda 4: 144, fig. 52/2 (1988); U.K.W.F., ed. 2: 325, t. 151 (1994); Lye in Fl. Ethiopia 6: 375, 208.1/8–10 (1997). Type: South Africa, Verkeerde valley, *Thunberg* 1267 (UPS, holo.)

Annual or sometimes perennial (see note), forming loose clumps. Leaves flabellate, up to 40 cm. long, 2 mm. wide; sheath gradually dilated to base, glabrous, smooth, green, brown at base, margin hyaline; ligule absent; lamina linear, glabrous; apex solid, paler, acute, slightly incurved. Peduncle 30–50(–75) cm. long, ± 2 mm. in diameter, ± terete with low longitudinal ridges; spike subspherical, becoming depressed-spherical with age, at maturity 5–12 mm. long, 7–14 mm. wide, dark brown; sterile bracts broadly ellipsoid to broadly obovate, rounded, the outer often split at the apex, brown, darker towards the middle and the apex; fertile bracts similar but paler and thinner, strongly concave, midrib keeled towards the retuse apex and apiculate. Lateral sepals boat-shaped, curved, glabrous, pale brown, keel entire, dark brown towards the acute or acuminate apex; corolla-lobes broadly obovate, ± 3.5 mm. long, 2.5 mm. wide; tube ± 4.5 mm. long. Filaments ± 0.5 mm. long; anthers ± 1 mm. long; staminodes bifurcate, much-branched. Ovary obovoid, 2.5 mm. long, 1.5 mm.; style 2 mm. long, branches ± 1 mm. long, much-branched, stigmas aggregated into a single mass. Seeds ellipsoid, 0.3 mm. long, 0.2 mm. in diameter, with 12–16 longitudinal ridges, cross-ridges also clear. Fig. 1/12.

UGANDA. Kigezi District: Muko, 4 Jan. 1962, *Morrison* 39!; Masaka District: Sese Is., Sozi, Dec. 1922, *Maitland* 337! & Lwera, 30 km. on Masaka–Kampala road, 11 Feb. 1971, *Kabuye* 340!

KENYA. Uasin Gishu District: plains S. of Eldoret, 20 June 1948, *Bogdan* 1725!; Naivasha/Kiambu District: near S. Kinangop, Sasamua Dam, 22 Oct. 1977, *M.G. Gilbert* 4875!; Kiambu District: Ondiri Swamp, 11 Apr. 1960, *Verdcourt* 2650!

TANZANIA. Bukoba, *Stuhlmann* 1088!; Iringa District: Iheme–Sao, 30 July 1933, *Greenway* 3421! & Dabaga Highlands, near Idete school, 31 Jan. 1971, *Mabberley* 639!

DISTR. **U** 2, 4; **K** 3, 4; **T** 1, 2, 5–7; widespread in the higher parts of Africa; plants attributed to this taxon in the broad sense also occur in India and China

HAB. Upland bogs and marshes; 1100–3000 m.

NOTE. This is a highly variable taxon which may in fact be a complex of several, and there is need for a comprehensive revision throughout its range. Two groups of specimens stand out from the rest. Specimens from bogs (often with *Sphagnum*) on the Lukwangule Plateau, Uluguru Mts. (Morogoro District) and elsewhere (e.g. *Pócs* 6823/H!, *Pócs & Csontas* 6081/L!, *Polhill & Wingfield* 4670! and *Bidgood et al.* 244!), at first sight appear distinct but are probably best placed here. They are perennial, sometimes with an elongated vertical rhizome, broader and shorter strongly distichous leaves than the normal form, and shorter peduncles. *Thulin & Tidigs* 111!, from the Cherangani Hills, (W. Suk/Elgeyo District), has similar leaves and habit, but peduncles as long as those of the normal form, as does *Schlieben* 3500!, also from the Lukwangule Plateau.

Another group, represented by *Haarer* 2074 (**T** 1), *Kahurananga et al.* 2755 (**T** 4), *Milne-Redhead & Taylor* 10849 (**T** 8) and *Drummond & Hemsley* 4688 (**U** 4), includes clearly annual plants with strongly distichous leaves with purple bases, and rather obtriangular spikes. Such material has often been confused with *X. straminea*, and named as *X. multicaulis* which is a synonym of the former. While distinct as a group, they are connected to the main group of specimens of *X. capensis* by intermediates.

15. **X. capillaris** *Malme* in Arkiv Bot. 24A, 5: 8 (1931). Types: Angola, between Mt. Amaral and Maria Pia, *Gossweiler* 1829 (BM!, K!, syn.) & Ikiuna "Caranda", *Gossweiler* 2472 (BM!, K!, syn.) & Kassuango, Kuiriri R., *Gossweiler* 3246 (BM!, K!, syn.) & *Gossweiler* 3267 (BM!, syn.)

Perennial forming dense tufts. Leaves markedly distichous at the base, up to 13 cm. long; sheaths ± 2.5 cm. long, 4 mm. wide near the base, pale brown, tinged red when young, smooth, margins and keel ciliate below, otherwise glabrous; ligule whitish, rounded, ± 2 mm. long; lamina ± 10 cm. long, 0.5 mm. wide, smooth, ± terete; apex apiculate, symmetric. Peduncle up to 30 cm. long, 0.5 mm. in diameter, smooth, terete; spike few-flowered, with one flower open at a time, ellipsoid when young, broader when old, ± 6 mm. long, 3 mm. in diameter, dark shining brown; outer sterile bracts broadly ovate, ± 4 mm. long, 2.2 mm. wide, inner ± 4.5 mm. long, 3 mm. wide, all concave, crustaceous, brown, apex rounded; fertile bracts similar, ± 6 mm. long, 4 mm. wide. Lateral sepals 5 mm. long, 1 mm. wide, the keel denticulate, particularly in the lower half; corolla yellow, tube 3 mm. long, lobes broadly ovate, 4 mm. long, 3 mm. wide, apex dentate. Stamens 3 mm. long; anther 2 mm. long; staminodes bifurcate, with bunches of long hairs. Ovary oblong, 2 mm. long, 0.5 mm. in diameter; style trifurcate near apex; stigmas much-lobed. Seeds ellipsoid, 0.5 mm. long, 0.3 mm. in diameter, with 12–14 longitudinal ridges. Fig. 1/13.

TANZANIA. Mpanda District: 61 km. on Uvinza–Mpanda road, 20 May 1997, *Bidgood et al.* 4096!
DISTR. T 4; Angola and Zambia
HAB. Large flat seepage area on grey to white sand; 1650 m.

NOTE. Only this one collection has been seen from the Flora area. The species is part of a poorly understood complex of tufted perennials with small spikes. These include *X. pumila* Rendle, from Angola, apparently with broader leaves and darker inflorescence-bracts. Unfortunately the type, *Welwitsch* 2471 (BM), is a heavily grazed or burned plant. *X. exigua* Malme, described from Zaïre is also superficially similar but has more flattened leaves with rugulose channels on both faces and fimbriate margins to the leaf-sheaths.

16. **X. subtilis** *Lock* in K.B. 53: 892 (1998). Type: Uganda, Masaka District, Bugabo, Lake Nabugabo, *Lye & Katende* 6525 (K!, holo., EA!, MAK, NHU, iso.)

Slender perennial. Leaves 8–12 cm. long, 0.5–1 mm. wide; sheaths rugulose, tapering to apex and expanded at the base, with smooth scarious margins which are ciliate particularly towards the base; ligule absent; lamina linear, flattened, rugulose; apex solid, acuminate. Peduncles 35–50 cm. long, ± 0.5 mm. in diameter, terete, smooth; spike subspherical, 5–7 mm. in diameter at maturity, dark brown; sterile bracts suborbicular, the lowest ± 2 mm. in diameter; fertile bracts ± 4 mm. in diameter, thinly coriaceous, 3-nerved, pale olive-brown, apex rounded, often splitting. Lateral sepals arcuate, 4–4.5 mm. long, the keel bluntly ciliate-denticulate, most markedly so towards the middle; corolla yellow, tube ± 5 mm. long, lobes elliptic, ± 4 mm. long, 2 mm. wide. Anthers ± 1 mm. long; staminodes bifurcate, the branches long-ciliate. Ovary ellipsoid, ± 3 mm. long; style ± 3 mm. long, 3-branched; stigmas many-lobed. Seeds broadly elliptic, ± 0.3 mm. long, 0.25 mm. in diameter, with more than 20 longitudinal ridges. Fig. 4.

UGANDA. Masaka District: Bugabo, Lake Nabugabo, 28 July 1971, *Lye & Katende* 6525! & Aug. 1935, *Chandler* 1358
TANZANIA. Bukoba, June 1931, *Haarer* 2022!; Kilwa District: Madaba, Ruvuma, 25 Mar. 1986, *de Leyser* 110!

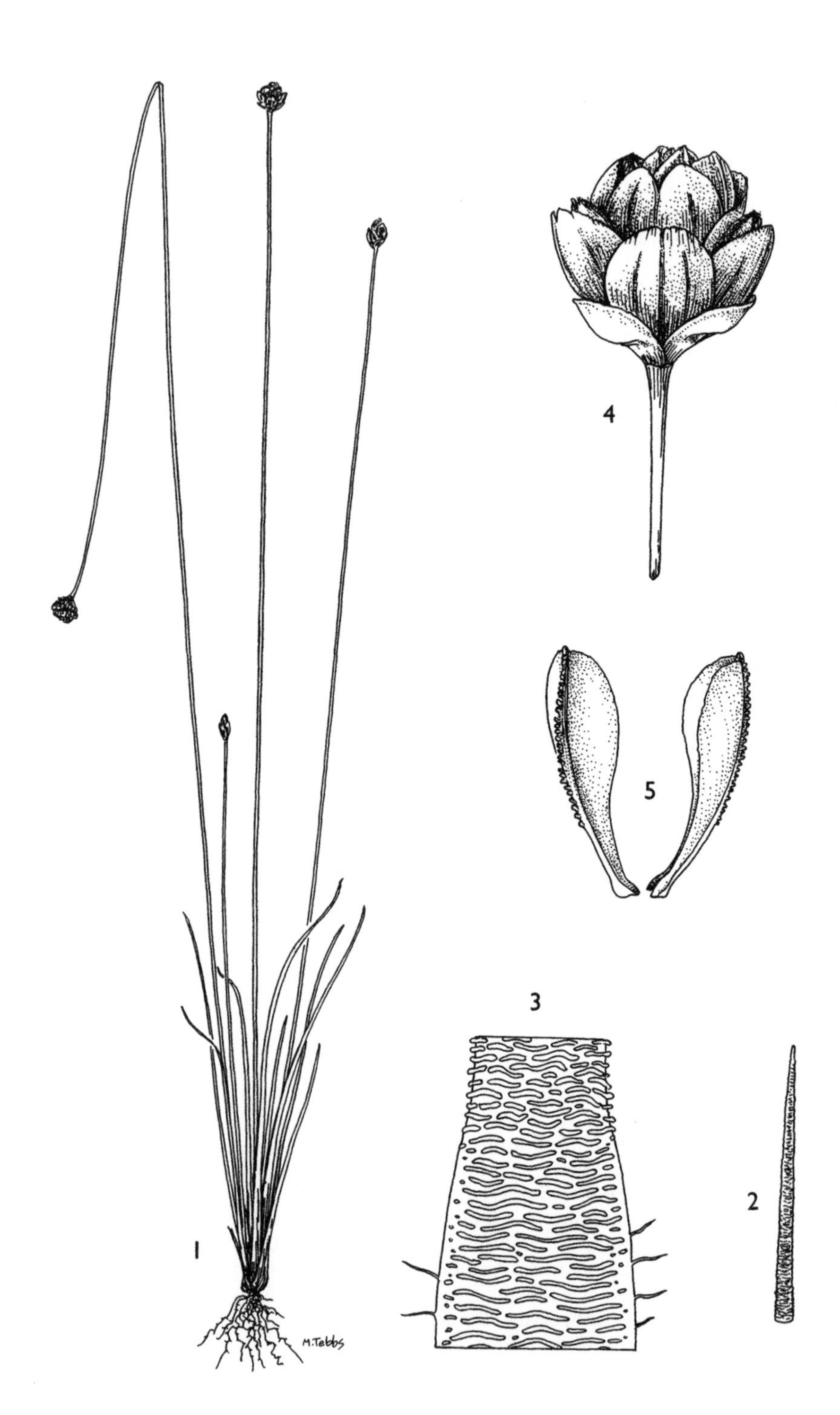

FIG. 4. *XYRIS SUBTILIS* — **1**, habit × $^2/_3$; **2**, leaf tip × 8; **3**, leaf surface pattern × 20; **4**, inflorescence × 6; **5**, lateral sepals × 8. Drawn by Margaret Tebbs from *Lye* 6525.

DISTR. **U** 4; **T** 1, 8; not definitely known elsewhere; very similar plants occur in Malawi and Zambia
HAB. Seasonally wet grassland; 450–1200 m.

NOTE. Differs from *X. peteri* in its more delicate stature, narrow rugulose leaves, broader lateral sepals and in the lack of rounded ligules. The disjunction between the records from the north-western quadrant of Lake Victoria and southern Tanzania is substantial, and the species should be looked for in the intervening areas.

Material from Uganda has been named as *X. welwitschii* Rendle, but the type of that species (*Welwitsch* 2465) has smooth thin straw-coloured inflorescence-bracts. See Lock in K.B. 53: 891 (1998).

17. **X. sp. A**

Perennial. Leaves up to 28 cm. long, 2 mm. wide; sheaths up to 8 mm. wide at the base, pale brown, with thinner paler margins, sulcate, smooth or slightly rugulose; lamina flattened, smooth, glabrous; apex acute, almost symmetric (most leaves broken or grazed). Peduncle up to 45 cm. or more tall, ± 1 mm. in diameter, smooth, terete or slightly ridged, particularly above; spike subspherical, becoming depressed-spherical at maturity, 6–9 mm. in diameter, golden olive-brown, with 1–2 flowers open simultaneously; outer sterile bracts broadly ovate, 4 mm. long, 2.5 mm. wide, convex, rounded at apex, crustaceous; inner sterile bracts 3.5 mm. long, 3.5 mm. wide, with 2 nerves, otherwise similar; fertile bracts suborbicular, strongly convex, 5.2 mm. long, 5.6 mm. wide, crustaceous, golden brown, with a slightly thickened median ridge, appressed. Lateral sepals narrowly boat-shaped, 4.5 mm. long, 1 mm. wide, the keel denticulate, particularly towards the base; corolla-tube 2 mm. long, lobes broadly elliptic, 3 mm. long, 2 mm. wide, dentate at the apex. Stamens 2 mm. long, anther 1 mm. long; staminodes of bunches of hairs. Ovary oblong, 2 mm. long, 0.6 mm. in diameter; style 3.5 mm. long, the uppermost 0.6 mm. trifid, the branches thickened; stigmas much-lobed and branched. Seeds ellipsoid, 0.4 mm. long, 0.2 mm. in diameter, with 14–18 longitudinal ridges. Fig. 1/14.

KENYA. Uasin Gishu District: near Kitale, Maboonde, Aug. 1955, *Tweedie* 1343!
DISTR. **K** 3; known only from this collection
HAB. "Drier part of swamp"; ± 1850 m.

NOTE. A very distinctive plant, known only from this collection. It has some resemblance to plants from N. Zambia (e.g. *Richards* 9336 - Zambia, Kawambwa District, Kawambwa–Mbereshi road, 18 Apr. 1957). Good material showing complete leaves, with notes on the growth form, is needed.

18. **X. peteri** *Poelln.* in Ber. Deutsch. Bot. Ges. 61: 204 (1944). Type: Burundi, E. of Niakassu, *Peter* 38255 (B!, holo.)

Perennial from slightly swollen base composed of persistent leaf-sheaths and leaf-bases. Leaves up to 25 cm. long, 1 mm. wide; sheaths blackish brown, longitudinally ridged, otherwise smooth, shiny, glabrous; ligule rounded, 2-lobed; lamina linear, smooth or very slightly rugulose; apex acuminate. Peduncles 25–38 cm. long, ± 1 mm. in diameter, glabrous, 2-ridged towards the apex; spike subspherical, ± 8 mm. in diameter; sterile bracts very broadly ellipsoid, ± 5 mm. long, 4 mm. wide, retuse at apex, thinly coriaceous, dark olive-brown; fertile bracts similar. Lateral sepals 6 mm. long, 1 mm. wide, apiculate, keel bluntly denticulate; corolla yellow, lobes broadly ovate, ± 4 mm. long, 3 mm. wide, dentate at the apex. Stamens ± 2.5 mm. long, including the 1 mm. long anthers. Style-branches trifid at the apex; stigmatic surfaces swollen and rounded. Ovary not seen. Seeds ellipsoid, 0.5 mm. long, 0.3 mm. in diameter, with ± 16 longitudinal ridges. Fig. 1/15.

TANZANIA. Iringa District: 92 km. on Iringa–Mbeya road, near Nyampara Mt., 26 Nov. 1975, *Leeuwenberg* 10850!; Njombe District: Elton Plateau, Ndumbi [Ndumbe] R., 11 Jan. 1957, *Richards* 7670! & Kitulo, 5 Mar. 1970, *Fuller* 141!

DISTR. **T** 7; Rwanda and Burundi
HAB. Upland swamp and grassland; 2250–2800 m.

NOTE. The measurements and descriptions of the flowers, fruit and seeds are taken from dissections attached to the type. *Richards* 7670 has immature seeds which appear more elongate than those of the type of *X. peteri*. Further material may show that it represents a different taxon.

Species 19–24. The small ephemeral African species of *Xyris* require further study on a continent-wide scale. It is not clear to what extent characters such as leaf rugosity vary within species, or whether they provide good distinctions. A fairly 'splitty' view has been taken here. *X. filiformis* Lam., from West Africa, is also part of this group but has a serrate keel to the lateral sepals. It has been recorded in error from the East African coast. Material from the highlands of Burundi has also been determined as *X. filiformis* but this seems unlikely. *X. scabridula* Rendle, from Angola, is very similar to *X. parvula* but has rugulose leaves and a few blunt cilia on the keel of the lateral sepals. *X. fugaciflora* Rendle has also been recorded from East Africa but these plants are here determined either as *X. huillensis* or as *X. schliebenii*.

19. **X. sp B**

Small annual. Leaves 5–8 cm. long, 1–1.5 mm. wide; sheaths rugulose, particularly towards the apex; ligule not seen; lamina glabrous, weakly rugulose on the margins, aristate at the apex. Peduncles 14–19 cm. long, 0.3–0.5 mm. in diameter, 4-winged, particularly towards the apex, with 2 wings more prominent than the rest; spike ellipsoid becoming subspherical, ± 3 mm. in diameter; lowest sterile bract obovate, 2.5 mm. long, 2 mm. wide, concave, pale red-brown, apiculate; second sterile bract similar, 2.8 mm. long, 2 mm. wide, aristate; fertile bracts broadly obovate, 3.2 mm. long, 3 mm. wide, strongly concave, apiculate, pale red-brown, apex and apiculus almost black. Lateral sepals narrowly boat-shaped, arcuate, 2.8 mm. long, 0.3 mm. wide, keel entire, apiculate. Corolla orange, lobes dentate at apex. Anthers 1 mm. long; staminodes bifurcate, each branch with a bunch of long hairs. Fruit and seeds unknown. Fig. 1/16.

TANZANIA. Tunduru District: 96 km. from Masasi, 21 Mar. 1963, *Richards* 17992!
DISTR. **T** 8; known only from this collection
HAB. Thin soil on granite outcrop; ± 900 m.

NOTE. Similar to *X. rubella* but differs in the aristate second bract, in the colour of the bracts, and in the cross-section of the peduncle. Named by Lewis as a form of *X. anceps* but very different from that species. Although at first I considered naming this after the collector, I do not now consider this appropriate, in view of the continuing confusion over species delimitation in the small African annual species of *Xyris*.
The details of the flower are taken from a bud.

20. **X. sp. C**

Small annual. Leaves 2.5–3 cm. long, 0.5 mm. wide, distichous; lamina smooth, glabrous, apex acute, ± symmetric. Peduncles up to 15 cm. long, 0.5 mm. in diameter, terete, weakly 2-ridged towards the apex; spike broadly ellipsoid, ± 7 mm. long, 4 mm. in diameter, becoming obtriangular with age; bracts elliptic, reddish brown with translucent pink edges, papillose on the outer surface, lanate-ciliate on the margins, particularly towards the apex; lower sterile bracts ± 3 mm. long, 2 mm. wide, upper ± 4 mm. long, 2 mm. wide; fertile bracts (immature) ± 4 mm. long, 2 mm. wide, papillose and pilose. Flowers, fruits and seeds not known. Fig. 1/17.

TANZANIA. Mpanda District: 56 km. on Uvinza–Mpanda road, 21 May 1997, *Bidgood et al.* 4404!
DISTR. **T** 4; known only from this collection
HAB. Large seepage areas in *Brachystegia* woodland with small pools, shallow grey sandy soil over ironstone; 1600 m.

NOTE. Distinctive in its reddish papillose pilose bracts. The material is sparse and still immature; more material is needed for description of the flowers, fruits and seeds.

21. **X. straminea** *L.A. Nilsson* in Öfvers. K. Vetensk.-Akad. Förhandl. Stockholm 1891: 153 (1891); N.E. Br. in F.T.A. 8: 19 (1901); Malme in E.J. 48: 304 (1912); Hepper in F.W.T.A., ed. 2, 3: 54, fig. 334A (1968); J. Lewis in Fl. Cameroun 2: 39, t. 6/9 (1981); U.K.W.F., ed. 2: 325 (1994); Lye in Fl. Ethiopia 6: 375, 208.1/1–7 (1997). Types: Nigeria, Nupe, near Bakona, and at Lom, *Barter* 764 (B, M, S, syn., K!, U, isosyn.)

Annual forming small tufts. Leaves linear, 4–8(–15) cm. long, 1–1.5 mm. wide, glabrous, sometimes rugulose towards the base, gradually tapering to the weakly curved apex. Peduncles up to 35 cm. long, 0.5 mm. in diameter, weakly 2-ridged particularly towards the apex, sometimes weakly rugulose on the ridges; spike narrowly ovoid to narrowly ellipsoid, 4.5–6.5 mm. long; sterile bracts 4, ovate, 3–4 mm. long, 1.7–2.5 mm. wide, acute, apiculate, pale brown or yellowish with a darker centre and apex, keeled towards the apex; fertile bracts similar but larger, ± 5 mm. long, 3 mm. Lateral sepals oblong, strongly keeled, ± 5 mm. long, 1.2 mm. wide, pale brown, keel entire, brown, darker particularly towards the apex, third sepal membranous, forming a hood over the bud; corolla-tube ± 2 mm. long, lobes oblong, ± 2 mm. long, 1 mm. Filament ligulate, 0.5 mm. long; anthers 0.5 mm. long; staminodes much-branched. Style-branches ± 1 mm. long; stigmas much-branched and lobed. Seeds broadly ellipsoid, ± 0.35 mm. long, 0.2 mm. in diameter, with 14–20 longitudinally ridges. Fig. 1/18.

UGANDA. W. Nile District: Koboko [Kobboko], *Eggeling* 1853!; Mbale District: Bugisu [Bugishu], Sipi, 31 Aug. 1932, *A.S. Thomas* 448! & Sebei, 1.5 km. SW. of Kapchorwa resthouse, 12 Oct. 1952, *G.H.S. Wood* 477!

KENYA. Northern Frontier Province: Lolokwi [Ol Lolokwe], opposite Subata Repeater Station, 14 Apr. 1979, *M.G. Gilbert* 5367!; Uasin Gishu District: Kaptagat [Kaptabat], Brockley Primary School, near Ministry of Agriculture station, 7 Oct. 1981, *M.G. Gilbert & Mesfin* 6443!; Nandi District: Lessos to Nandi Hills, ± 12 km. from Nandi Hills, 13 Oct. 1981, *M.G. Gilbert & Mesfin* 6737!

TANZANIA. Bukoba District: Biharamulo road, 5 km. S. of Bukoba, Aug. 1931, *Haarer* 2074!; Kigoma District: 5 km. from Kigoma on Kasulu road, 11 July 1960, *Verdcourt* 2787!; Songea District: 6.5 km. W. of Songea, 13 June 1956, *Milne-Redhead & Taylor* 10801!

DISTR. **U** 1, 3, 4; **K** 1, 3; **T** 1, 4, 5, 7, 8; Sierra Leone eastwards to Kenya and south to Zambia and South Africa

HAB. Shallow soil over rock, flushes, seasonal swamps among grass tussocks; 900–2400 m.

SYN. *X. multicaulis* N.E. Br. in F.T.A. 8: 20 (1901); Malme in E.J. 48: 304 (1912). Type: Malawi, Namasi, *Cameron* 51 (K!, holo.)

NOTE. A widespread annual species of ephemeral habitats, often growing mixed with other species of the genus, particularly *X. rubella.*

22. **X. rubella** *Malme* in E.J. 48: 303 (1912); Hepper in K.B. 21: 424 (1968) & in F.W.T.A., ed. 2, 3: 54 (1968). Types: Namibia, Damara, Okahandja, *Dinter* 944 (B!, S, SAM, syn.); Tanzania, Kilwa District, Orero to Kilwa Karingi, *Braun* in *Herb. Amani* 1326 (EA!, S, syn.)

Small annual, forming loose tufts. Leaves distichous, 2–6 (–14) cm. long, 1–1.5 mm. wide, glabrous, rugulose, apex solid, acuminate to aristate. Peduncle 8–20(–30) cm. long, 0.5 mm. in diameter, rugulose, 2-winged, particularly toward the apex; spike subglobose, ± 3 mm. in diameter; lowest bracts broadly elliptic, 1.3 mm. long, 1 mm. wide; sterile bracts broadly spathulate, ± 1.8 mm. long, 1.3 mm. wide, apiculate, smooth, vinous-red to reddish-brown; fertile bracts broadly elliptic, ± 2.7 mm. long, 2.4 mm. wide, keeled, pale red-brown with a darker keel, smooth, apiculate. Lateral sepals arcuate, folded, pale brown, 2.2 mm. long, 0.5 mm. wide, apiculate, keel smooth; corolla-tube 2 mm. long, lobes suborbicular, ± 1.8 mm. in diameter. Stamens 0.8 mm. long; filament 0.4 mm. long; anthers 0.4 mm. long, divergent at the base; staminodes bifurcate, ± 0.5 mm. long. Ovary obovoid, 1.5 mm. long; style 1 mm. long, branches 1 mm. long; stigma branches recurved. Seeds ellipsoid, 0.3 mm. long, 0.15 mm. in diameter, with 12–14 longitudinal ridges. Fig. 1/19.

TANZANIA. Dodoma District: 42.5 km. S. of Itigi station on Chunya road, 20 Apr. 1964, *Greenway & Polhill* 11668!; Uzaramo District: Dar es Salaam, 10 km. W. of city centre, Mabibo–Kisukuro road, N. of Mabibo Primary School, 6 June 1996, *Faden et al.* 96/32; Songea District: Nangurukuru Hill, 26 km. E. of Songea, 8 Apr. 1956, *Milne-Redhead & Taylor* 9552!

DISTR. **T** 5–8; probably elsewhere in Africa but distribution not clearly understood because of confusion with *X. schliebenii*

HAB. Shallow soils on rocky outcrops, between grass tussocks in seasonally wet grassland, often with *X. straminea* and species of *Eriocaulon*; 50–1650 m.

SYN. *X. capensis* 'paedogenic variant' sensu J. Lewis & Oberm. in F.S.A. 4(2): 2 (1985)

NOTE. Lewis & Oberm. regarded this as a dwarf starved form of *X. capensis*, flowering prematurely. Several features distinguish it, however, including the form and colour of the bracts, the usually aristate leaf-apex, and the consistently rugulose leaves and peduncles.

23. **X. schliebenii** *Poelln.* in Ber. Deutsch. Bot. Ges. 61: 204 (1944). Type: Tanzania, Kilwa District, Mbwera [Mbuera], *Schlieben* 2435 (B!, holo., BM!, iso.)

Small annual attaining 30 cm. in height, very similar to the previous species, but differing in the smooth (not rugulose) sheaths and laminas, in the incurved, obtuse, sometimes mucronate (not straight and aristate) lamina and peduncle-sheath apices, and in the more strongly keeled emarginate and apiculate fertile bracts. Fig. 1/20.

TANZANIA. Dodoma District: Kazikazi, 5 May 1932, *B.D. Burtt* 3599!; Iringa, just N. of township, 15 July 1956, *Milne-Redhead & Taylor* 11163!; Tunduru District: ± 1 km. E. of Songea District boundary, 6 June 1956, *Milne-Redhead & Taylor* 10657!

DISTR. **T** 4, 5, 7, 8; probably widespread in Africa but unclear due to confusion with the previous species

HAB. Seasonally wet grassland, margins of seasonal pools and marshes, often on or around rock outcrops; 800–1650 m.

NOTE. See the comments under the previous species. It is worth noting that *B.D. Burtt* 3599 and *Bidgood et al.* 4042 include plants well within the normal size range of *X. capensis*, but which are still quite distinct.

24. **X. parvula** *Malme* in E.J. 48: 304 (1912). Type: Tanzania, Rufiji District, Mafia I., *Kränzlin* 2983 (B!, holo., EA!, iso.)

Small annual. Leaves 2–3 cm. long, 1 mm. wide; sheaths smooth, glabrous, brown, gradually dilated to the base, rather abruptly tapering above; ligule absent or up to 0.5 mm. long; lamina linear, smooth, glabrous; apex acute to obtuse, incurved. Peduncles 6–13 cm. long, smooth, glabrous, terete or slightly 2-ridged towards the apex; mature spike ellipsoid, 3–4 mm. long, 1.5–2 mm. in diameter, dark brown; outer sterile bracts very broadly ovate, 1.5 mm. long, 1.3 mm. wide, concave; inner sterile bracts suborbicular, 2 mm. long, 2 mm. wide, concave; fertile bracts suborbicular, ± 2.5 mm. long, 2.5 mm. wide, concave, brown. Lateral sepals arcuate, 2.5 mm. long, 0.5 mm. wide, acute, keel entire. Filament ± 1 mm. long; anthers ± 1 mm. long, sagittate at the base. Ovary ± 1.2 mm. long; style 1.5 mm. long, 3-branched. Seeds (immature only seen) ellipsoid, ± 0.25 mm. long, with 12–14 longitudinal ridges. Fig. 1/21.

KENYA. Kilifi District: Mida, Sept. 1929, *R.M. Graham* 2113!

TANZANIA. Rufiji District: Mafia I., Kilindoni, 6 Aug. 1936, *Fitzgerald* 5212/4! & 0.5 km. E. of Kilindoni airfield, 18 Dec. 1977, *Wingfield* 4554!

DISTR. **K** 7; **T** 6; Mozambique
HAB. Sandy seasonally wet places near the sea; 0–10 m.

NOTE. Details of the staminodes, corolla and styles are unclear and good material in spirit is needed.
R.M. Graham 2113 was seen by Malme who noted that the leaves were somewhat wider than those of the type – this may well be because it was in good condition when collected!

DOUBTFUL SPECIES

25. **X. aberdarica** *Malme* in N.B.G.B. 8: 663 (1924). Type: Kenya, Naivasha District, Aberdare Mts., Kinangop Forest Station, *R.E. & T.C.E. Fries* 2905 (UPS!, holo., K!, iso.)

Probably perennial. Leaves ± 5 cm. long; sheaths black-brown, glabrous, smooth; ligule absent; lamina weakly rugulose, glabrous, linear. Peduncle ± 10 cm. long; inflorescence-bracts black-brown, coriaceous. Flowers not seen. Seeds ellipsoid. Fig. 1/22.

The isotype at Kew is very poor, and the holotype at UPS, although better, is still sparse and apparently from a grazed plant. Lewis placed *X. aberdarica* in the synonymy of *X. obscura*, but the bracts, although dark, are thinner, smooth rather than papillose, and have no apiculus. In its bracts and general appearance it is closest to *X. peteri* but differs in the very dark bracts, small stature, and somewhat rugulose leaf-sheaths.

INDEX TO XYRIDACEAE

No new names validated in this part

T - #0068 - 090625 - C0 - 244/170/2 - PB - 9789061913856 - Gloss Lamination